THE FANTASTIC FAIRGROUND

by

BERNARD GOSS

Music by CHRIS HAMEL–COOKE

Lyrics by DENIS BON[...]

This b[...]

library, a[...]

home readi[...]

SAMU[EL]   The libr[...]   FRENCH

[...] an[...]

LONDON

NEW YORK   TORONTO   SYDNEY   HOLLYWOOD

THE FANTASTIC FAIRGROUND

The play is written for eight actors, some of whom play more than one character. Music and musical effects, which are available from Samuel French Ltd, might be provided by Mr Barker. He could play a guitar, banjo, piano or even a small organ, and be present for all the action. If this is not possible there might be a small "group" or band either on the stage or in the pit.

The Fantastic Fairground is conceived as a theatrical equivalent of a children's comic paper. Its story is at times exciting, funny, frightening, musical, mad and sometimes lyrical, executed in a simple setting with tremendous ingenuity, colour and speed.

Professionally, the play has been produced successfully on arena and proscenium arch stages, as well as in small studio spaces. Whatever the physical presentation there should be a close proximity between actors and audiences thus encouraging a strong relationship, so that audience participation can grow naturally out of the story—the most important element of the piece. With such a simple text, and the suggested emphasis being on colour and movement, the producer should make sure the narrative is sharply focused and clear. Suggestions for scenic necessities are made at appropriate points in the text, but as any successful production should have its own unique improvisational spontaneity about it, the decision of each individual director is important.

The **Usherettes' Duet** on page 33 is included as an optional extra. It was originally included as Floss and Brunhilda had become popular, but if very young children are in the audience this song may bore them so inclusion of it is left to each director's discretion.

The author would like to thank the team of *The Rose Bruford College* students who worked with him on the original improvisation which inspired this script.

THE FANTASTIC FAIRGROUND

(Suggested casting for eight actors)

Brunhilda, an usherette in the Waxwork Chamber **A Medieval Lady** **Lady Melanie** **Floss,** an usherette in the Waxwork Tent	Actress 1
Terry, a young boy or girl	Actor 1
Jack of All Trades	Actor 2
Professor Waxman	Actor 3
Grandpa **Splodge,** an usher in the Waxwork Chamber **"Grab" Machine** **Eastern God** **"Man of Mystery"** **Mathew Mudwinkle,** the Merry-Go-Round owner **Leader of the Chase**	Actor 4
Tall Tom, the Highwayman **Rifle-Range Man** **Spivver,** an usher in the Waxwork Chamber **Snake** **"Test Your Strength" Machine** **Dr Quack** **Arthur,** a Merry-Go-Round horse	Actor 5
Mr Barker	Actor 6

ACT I

During the opening music—melodies used in the show—the actors have entered in their clothes which are simple, colourful and possibly uniform. They chat and play with the Audience. The acting area is a colourful open space for the beginning—only a fairground organ or space for the Musician is necessary

Mr Barker, who has now put on something which distinguishes his character, addresses the audience

Mr Barker Hello then, boys and girls, I'm Mr Barker; welcome to the Fantastic Fairground! Hold on tightly for the Adventure of the Age!

ROLL UP, ROLL UP (SONG)   **1**

The Company	Come roll up, the Fair is calling:
	Bright lights welcome you to Candyland.
	Can you hear the barker's bawling—
Waxman	People buying from a hot pie stand?
The Company	Come roll up and join the fun.
	Sing along—the Fair's begun.

Mr Barker Enjoy the thrills and spills of the Fair. Hear the laughter, see the lights, and join in the songs.

Jack and Terry	Come and see the neons flashing;
	See the dancers sent from the East,
Quack and Grandpa	Hear the sweet girls' popcorn cracking—
Waxman	Step this way for a lollipop feast!
The Company	Come roll up and join the fun.
	Sing along: the Fair's begun.

By now the actors are beginning to "act" parts of the song using simple articles of costume they find behind the scenery

> There's a band that's swinging,
> There'll be people singing,
> And a big wheel spinning—on high!
> See the swing-boat swaying,
> Hear the organ playing.
> There'll be fun all evening; how the time will fly!

Mr Barker (*to the Audience*) Like to learn the chorus? Right! Tell you what we'll do. I'll say the line—and you say it after me. "Come roll up, and join the fun!" (*Repeat*) "Sing along: the Fair's begun." (*Repeat*)

Now let's try it with the music! Sing the chorus and we'll go on with the next verse.

The Audience does so

The Company	Come roll up and join the fun.
	Sing along; the Fair's begun.
	If you want your fortune told you
	Find the man who's all dressed in black.
Man of Mystery	With his secrets he'll enfold you
	As his crystal ball takes you back.
The Company	Come roll up and join the fun;
	Sing along; the Fair's begun.
Terry and Jack	See the midgets prancing and the stilt-men dancing,
	And the ghost train laughing—at night
Floss and Brunhilda	There'll be monkeys playing, there'll be horses
	neighing,
The Company	And the crowds all shouting as the wrestlers fight.

Two of the actors perform wrestling throws—eventually they all join in the fun

Mr Barker Break it up now, boys—come on, girls, break it up. Clear a space, everyone, 'cos the Adventure's about to begin.

All except Mr Barker exit

Now! Let's begin the story! Long before the Fairground ever appeared.

One of the actors, now dressed as Jack of All Trades, a typical "handy-man", enters. He is young, lively and his pockets are filled with useful tools. The way he acts suggests someone extraordinary

First of all, I want you to meet a friend of mine, who'll soon be a friend of yours. Boys and girls, may I introduce—Jack?

Jack bows to the audience

Or—to give him his full title—Jack of All Trades . . .

Some of the other actors jump out from behind the scenery

Waxman
Quack } (*rudely*) And Master of None! (*Speaking together*)

They jump back. Jack is upset

Mr Barker Take no notice, Jack. (*To the Audience*) There's not a thing he can't do—'andy round the place he is!

Jack is more cheerful now, and proceeds to demonstrate the following actions

That's right, Jack. He'll dig the garden for you—clean the windows—

oil the works—any job worth doing, he'll do! Not much to say for himself, mind you. Got a secret 'as Jack—

Jack grins

—and he's keeping it all to himself.

Terry enters. Terry is either a boy or girl of about twelve years—very enthusiastic for adventure

Here's young Terry. Bit bored is Terry—lives down the street with his Grandpa—not many friends to talk to.

Terry (*eagerly*) Hey, Jack. Where's the adventure?

Jack is mending something, possibly the organ or one of the musical instruments

The *fantastic* adventure. You *promised* me!

Jack No time, Terence [or Theresa].

Terry (*annoyed*) Terry!

Jack There's too much work—for your grandpa.

He gestures towards the place where Grandpa will enter

Grandpa enters. He is old, kind and with a very obvious beard. He could wear a uniform

Mr Barker Here's the old man now—works in a museum. Nice old man—fond of his treasures.

The "statue" of the actress as Lady Melanie is brought forward (actually the actress who plays her later)

Grandpa Jack, give this statue a dust, will you? Lady Melanie was a good woman. I hate to see her face dirty.

Jack dusts the "statue" with an enormous piece of cloth from his pocket

Terry (*with intense curiosity*) Grandpa, who *was* Lady Melanie?

Grandpa One of your ancestors, my boy. I like this statue of her—(*mysteriously*)—even though the pearls *are* missing.

Terry Pearls, Grandpa?

Grandpa Her pearl necklace. (*Explaining*) Eight black pearls from a pirate's hoard—strung together to make the finest necklace. (*Sighing, as he refers to the "statue"*) But this was carved after they were gone.

Terry Gone!

Jack is interested now

Grandpa Stolen. Stolen by Tall Tom.

Terry (*excitedly*) Grandpa! (*Referring to the Audience*) Tell us all about it. Please!

Grandpa, Terry and Jack settle down

Grandpa (*in true story-telling manner*) Tall Tom was a highwayman, the bravest in these parts.

The other actors represent the characters of the story, dressed in easily identifiable costume. Tall Tom enters. Music heightens the action

It was said that he stole the pearls at the Hundred Years Fair. Nobody knows where it came from or where it went, but since olden days every hundred years there has been a fair on our common; and two hundred years ago, Lady Melanie's pearl necklace was stolen at the Fair.

The statue of Lady Melanie comes "alive" and joins her eighteenth-century Maid, who enters, to re-enact her story. The Lights gradually fade over the rest of the stage

Tall Tom had been standing nearby—

A Stranger has entered. He points at Tall Tom

—and he was found guilty.

Tall Tom exits

But when they searched him, he didn't have the pearls. Some say he hid them in the Fairground before his arrest—others say he was innocent. But later he was hanged—

Lady Melanie and her Maid look off-stage at the hanging. They lower their heads

—and if he was innocent, it was never proved.

Lady Melanie and Maid exit

Terry (*worried*) Do *you* think he was guilty, Grandpa?
Grandpa He robbed the rich—to feed the poor. But the Lady Melanie's pearls—I don't know.

There is only the figure of the Stranger left now

It was discovered afterwards that the man who accused Tall Tom was a stranger, that he'd been wandering through the Fairground the night before.

The Stranger exits

Terry Who *was* the Stranger?
Grandpa Nobody knew, and nobody knows. The mystery remains. Folk say that if anyone ever finds the Lady Melanie's necklace, the truth will be revealed.

Jack moves to a grave-stone which has been set in the darkness

Terry (*jumping up with excitement*) Grandpa, we'll find the necklace. (*Referring to the Audience*) We'll find the truth, won't we? Jack!

Terry looks round for Jack

Grandpa He's over there—on the Common.

It is quite dark now

Terry (*running to him*) Jack, what have you found?

Grandpa Be careful, Terry. If Tall Tom was guilty you'll have searched for nothing, and if he was innocent you may be in grave danger.

Grandpa exits

Jack (*referring to the object*) It's a grave-stone. Some sort of monument. (*He cleans it with a rag from his pocket*)

Terry (*seeing some words*) What does it say?

Jack (*reading*) "Here lies Tall Tom, hanged for the theft of a Lady's pearls."

Terry (*strongly*) He didn't do it. He didn't steal the pearls. Jack, help us to prove he didn't. If we could only find the necklace. Where . . . ?

Terry notices that Jack has become even more interested in the grave-stone

What is it?

Jack A date. One—seven—seven . . . Seventeen hundred and seventy-five. (*He looks at Terry*) Eighteen hundred and seventy-five . . . Nineteen hundred——(*The date should refer to the current year*)

Terry —and seventy-five. That's NOW! (*Beginning to be frightened*) Jack! It's *time*—time for the Fairground! (*Quietly*) Once every hundred years they say. Jack, I'm frightened.

Jack stands up and seems to beckon into the shadows

What are you doing? Come on. Let's hide.

Jack (*holding him*) Keep still, and *watch*!

The other actors, dressed in simple fairground clothes, appear and move towards Terry and Jack. Scenery for a Fairground may be revealed now— a shooting-target, etc. (see Property List, p. 46). Mr Barker and the others sing

ROLL UP, ROLL UP (SONG)   2

The Company Roll up, roll up, roll up,
The Fair is calling you,
We've a Speedway and games to play
And Helter-skelters, too.
There are lots of things to do here
And lots of things to see,

> For everyone is welcome,
> And everything is free.
> A Fairground's the world
> For little boys and girls;
> The world is an oyster—
> Search for the pearls.

All move, suggesting the following lyrics

> Climb up high on the Big Wheel,
> Fly in a plane,
> Do it while there's still some time,
> You won't see us again.
> Ride the Ghost Train,
> Shoot a rocket high,
> Leave the Fairground
> And touch the sky.

Terry Isn't this fantastic? That's it. It's the Fantastic Fairground.

The Company Roll up, roll up, roll up,
> The Fair is calling you
> We've got ice-cream and candy floss,
> And toffee apples, too.
> There are lots of things to do here
> And lots of things to see.
> For everyone is welcome,
> And everything is free.

Mr Barker A Fairground's the world
> For little boys and girls;

The Company The world is an oyster—
> Search for the pearls.

Stillness. Terry and Jack face the Fairground people. Suddenly, the Rifle-Range Man moves forward

Rifle-Range Man Come on, lad. Try your aim at the Rifle Range. To Join the Fantastic Fairground—shoot a *bull's-eye*!

Terry (*to the Audience*) The Fairground's waiting for us. We can't go back now. Remember—this is the Adventure of the Age. We've got to find those pearls—they must be somewhere, even after two hundred years. (*To the Rifle-Range Man*) Give me the rifle—I've got to win! (*He takes the rifle and takes aim at a large bull's-eye*)

Rifle-Range Man Three chances—that's all, lad.

Jack tries to guide Terry's aim for him

Terry No, Jack. *I'LL* do it. I must—on my own.

Terry fires, and misses

(*Disappointed*) Missed!

Rifle-Range Man Two shots to go!

Terry aims and shoots, but misses again

Terry One shot left . . . (*He looks at Jack*) Please?

Jack guides his aim carefully

Rifle-Range Man The last chance.

Terry fires, and wins

A bull's-eye. Collect your prize.

Terry (*doing so*) Thanks. (*Inspecting it*) It's a purse. Nothing inside.

Jack (*taking hold of the purse*) Yes, there is. It's a pearl. (*He holds it up*)

Terry (*realizing*) A *black pearl*! The necklace must have been broken——

Jack —And the pearls hidden in different parts of the Fairground! (*Looking at the pearl*) But it's the beginning.

Terry We mustn't lose it. You have it.

Jack It might drop out of my pockets. Let one of the boys and girls look after it.

Terry It might drop out of their pockets too.

Jack looks round and sees some small numbered boxes on a stall

Jack Not if we put it in a box with the number on—one. (*He takes a numbered box from one of the stalls*) There. (*He finds a child in the Audience*) Would you look after the first pearl? Don't lose it—it's treasure. And don't give it to anyone else, unless I say so.

WHERE CAN THE NEXT ONE BE? (SONG)   3

We've found Number One in a place so strange
In a bull's-eye, centre of a rifle range.
Now there's one more thing that's puzzling me
Where can the next one be—be—be?
Where can the next one be?

Jack comes back to Terry

Now—to find the others!

Terry Oh Jack, they could be anywhere in the Fairground.

Jack Let's start looking then.

Fairground music starts up. Jack and Terry wander among the fairground people. They find one of the actresses dressed as a Balloon Lady

Have a balloon—they're free. (*He hands a balloon to Terry*)

The actor who will eventually play Waxman enters with candy floss

Terry Candy floss!

Jack Have some later. Have a go at Hoopla!

Terry throws an enormous hoopla ring over it. The "Waxman actor" finds a large ice-cream and holds it up

There now—first time!

Terry What an enormous ice-cream!

Jack pulls Terry away

"*Waxman*" *exits*

Jack No time for that—we've got to find a clue.

An actor with a top hat and a whip enters. He is the Merry-go-round Man.

Merry-go-round Man Any more for the Merry-go-round? Up and down you'll go on my lovely horses—thoroughbreds the lot of them!

Terry Do you think *he* might help us?

Merry-go-round Man Round you'll go—always coming back to the same place.

Another actor—as Dr Quack—enters. He carries a suitcase full of medicine bottles—a shifty, quick-witted character

Terry Huh! That's not very cheerful.

Dr Quack Listen to the wise words of your old friend, Dr Quack. Drink my medicine from the jungles of Africa, a secret recipe from a witch-doctor himself. Measles, septic knee, there's nothing I can't cure.

Jack Don't you believe it.

Terry (*going to the Waxwork Tent*) What's down here?

Dr Quack No! Don't go in there! Nobody goes in there!

Terry Why not?

Dr Quack That's the Waxwork Tent. People go in, but never come out.

There is the sound of wicked laughter from inside the tent—the light is fading and there is thunder in the distance. Dr Quack, Terry and Jack are the only ones left

Some say they're turned into *wax*!

Jack Who does it belong to?

Dr Quack (*running away*) Professor Waxman!

Dr Quack exits. A figure with a large umbrella emerges from the tent. It is Waxman

Jack Come on. Let's get out of here.

Terry I'm not frightened. He might be able to help us.

Terry approaches the figure. Jack pulls back into the shadows

(*Politely*) Professor Waxman?

There is the sound of thunder

Waxman What a nasty shower!

Terry (*beginning to feel nervous*) Yes.

Waxman You can share this. (*He holds up his umbrella*)

Terry It's not all that wet.

Waxman You'll catch cold.

Terry Aaaaaaaaaattttttchoooooooooo!

Waxman (*nauseatingly sympathetic*) There! Come and be dry with me. An old man like me looks after himself.

Terry You're not that old.

Waxman (*with evil*) I'm centuries old!

By working the catch he tries to catch Terry inside his umbrella

Terry (*escaping*) Ohhh! (*Looking round for his friend*) Jack!

Waxman (*apologetically*) The catch slipped. (*He tries to trap him again*)

Terry (*running away*) I don't want to share your umbrella. Leave me alone . . . Jack! Help!

Jack (*appearing from the shadows*) I'm here!

Jack pulls the umbrella over Waxman's head

Waxman (*struggling*) Ahhhhhhhhhhhh!

Jack (*taking Terry by the hand*) Quick!

Jack and Terry rush away. Spivver, Splodge, Brunhilda and Floss, the Waxwork Ushers, appear. They call out to the Audience

Spivver Any more for the Waxwork!

Brunhilda Step this way for the Waxwork Tent!

Splodge See the waxed-up wonders of the World!

Floss All stuck up! Without a word between them!

Waxman escapes from his umbrella

Spivver (*seeing Waxman emerging from the umbrella*) Look. 'Ere's a new customer.

Splodge (*sulkily*) About time!

Floss (*realizing who it is*) It's Professor Waxman.

Brunhilda Professor! (*Bossily*) Into line, you lot, turn around, face front.

The four line up. Brunhilda is big and the "sergeant-major" of the group. Spivver is cunning and sly. Splodge and Floss are vague and nervous

All present and correct. (*Stepping forward*) Chief Usherette Brunhilda!

Spivver Second-in-command—Spivver.

Splodge Third-in-command—Splodge.

Floss (*pathetically*) Fourth-in-command—Assistant Usherette Floss!

Spivver (*brightly*) We thought you were a customer!

Waxman (*with terrible incredibility*) Me! A *customer!*

Splodge (*stepping forward: in desperation*) We need 'em. There's no-one left to watch the waxworks.

Floss (*horrified at his insolence*) Splodge!

Splodge (*to Waxman*) You've waxified so many people, there's more wax-works than customers!

Spivver Don't be rude.

Splodge (*looking at the Audience*) I thought at first he'd waxified this lot, by the look of them. Talk about the Chamber of Horrors!
Brunhilda Get into *line*!
Waxman (*to Splodge*) You disapprove of my methods?
Splodge We'll be out of business soon.
Waxman (*working himself into a rage*) I will waxify *who* I like *when* I like—including YOU—NOW!
Floss Oh no, not that!
Waxman Bring me the *WAXIFIER!*

Spivver rushes off. Floss and Splodge panic, while Brunhilda ingratiates herself into Waxman's confidence

Floss (*to Splodge*) You've gone and done it now.
Brunhilda Never was any good anyway. Stubbed his cigarette on the Queen of Sheba. Now she's melted—all of a heap.
Floss (*protectingly*) He never!
Brunhilda Yes he did. (*Turning to Waxman*) And there's something else you should know, Professor Waxman.
Splodge Old Tell-tale!
Brunhilda When he got lost in the dark, he broke off one of Beethoven's fingers and used it as a candle!

Spivver runs in with the Waxifier, a larger kind of fly-spray, very baroque and colourful

Spivver 'Ere we are, Professor. All nice and polished.
Waxman (*taking it lovingly*) Ah! My secret weapon. The Waxifier! Now. Before I squirt the solution, who do we need in the Waxworks?
Brunhilda (*jerking Splodge's arm into a salute*) A soldier.
Floss (*delicately placing him in an arabesque*) A ballet dancer!
Spivver (*giving him a kick*) A monster—from Outer Space!
Floss Oh! Don't let him go as that!
Waxman (*scrutinizing him*) The face isn't right.
Splodge I'm too handsome.
Floss Yes, you are. Before you go, give me a kiss.

At this thought Splodge makes a hideous face. Waxman squirts the Waxifier. The others get out of the way

Waxman There. (*He surveys the new waxwork*) That's a good morning's work.
Spivver (*aghast*) What a way to go!
Brunhilda If I was a waxwork, I'd like to be Winston Churchill.
Floss Snow White for me. (*To Brunhilda*) What about a fairy?
Brunhilda I'd rather be a wicked witch.
Waxman (*having trouble with the Waxifier*) The handle's a bit stiff.
Brunhilda (*chattily*) If *you* were a waxwork, Spivver, what would . . .?

Waxman accidentally squirts the Waxifier

Oh!

Spivver, who was just fastening his shoe-lace, has been waxified in this position

Brunhilda (*touching his bottom*) Wax. It gets you in the end.

Floss (*sadly*) All our friends seem to go this way.

Waxman There's someone else going that way, too. The little boy that's noseying around the Fair—he'd look good in wax—as Peter Pan.

Floss (*pleasantly*) I like Peter Pan.

Waxman (*horrified*) You like *children*?

Floss (*frightened*) Oh, no—no, Professor Waxman!

Brunhilda (*with relish, as she surveys the Audience*) I *hate them all*!

Waxman Let's torture him first.

Brunhilda I know. Put him on the Big Wheel, and make it go round so fast that he falls off.

Floss (*bravely*) Throw rice pudding at him.

Brunhilda (*sarcastically*) No—he might like it.

Floss What?

Brunhilda (*nastily*) Rice pudding!

Waxman I have it. Sweets—toffees—I shall disguise myself as the Sweet Lady.

Brunhilda Ooooh, I ought to have known. (*Flatteringly*) "Meet the Man with Many Disguises."

Waxman (*gleefully*) I'll become very sweet—and sugary. I must disguise myself—now.

Waxman exits. Brunhilda and Floss settle down for a chat

Brunhilda Isn't the Professor clever.

Floss (*doubtfully*) Is he?

Brunhilda I mean . . . who else would have had the brains?

Floss (*looking sadly at the waxified Splodge*) Splodge would—if he'd had the chance.

Brunhilda Oh no he wouldn't. (*She looks at Spivver*) Poor Spivver.

Floss How do we know all children like sweets?

Brunhilda (*hypocritically, as she sees Waxman returning in his disguise*) They must do, if the Professor said so.

Waxman enters, dressed as Sweet Lady

Waxman All right, girls, cut your cackles. (*He pushes them behind a stall*) Here comes the brat now. Find some sweets for him to suck—the little sucker! (*He giggles madly*)

Brunhilda and Floss arrange sweet trays they find in a stall

Terry and Jack enter

Terry Who's that?
Jack I'm not sure, let's go and see.

Music begins again

Waxman There is a land not far away
        Over Lemonade Sea,
        Where all the stars are toffee bars
        And lollipops grow on a tree.
        Peanuts and pop are yours for free,
        The grass is golden not green,
        Just reach for the moon and you will see
        It's only a peppermint cream.
Terry Jack! (*Running to Waxman*) Sweets!
Jack Careful, Terry.
Waxman (*taking hold of Terry; singing*)
        So come along and hold my hand,
        You haven't got time to sleep.
        But if it's too far to Sugarland
        I'll sell you sweets very cheap!
        Sixpence will buy for girl or boy

He takes a bag of sweets from one of the trays

        A bag of coconut whirls,
        Or aniseed balls that you'll enjoy . . .
Mr Barker (*interrupting the song*) They look as lovely as pearls.

The song finishes. Stillness

Terry (*already sucking one of the aniseed balls*) This doesn't taste like an
aniseed ball—it's not melting. (*Taking the sweet out of his mouth*) In
fact it doesn't look like a sweet.
Jack (*taking hold of it*) It's a pearl.
Terry Fancy finding a pearl in a bag of aniseed balls. That's *two*!
Waxman (*in a rage*) Aaaaaaagh!

Waxman, Brunhilda and Floss disappear behind the stall

Terry Put this in a box as well, Jack, and ask one of our friends to look
after it.

*Terry and Jack take another box and go into the Audience to deliver the
pearl*

Waxman (*dragging Brunhilda and Floss from behind the stall*) Who gave
me that bag of aniseed balls?
Brunhilda (*quickly*) She did! Floss!
Floss But *you* gave them to *me*!
Brunhilda Didn't.
Floss Did!

Waxman Quiet! Or I'll waxify you both—as the Ugly Sisters.

Terry and Jack return to the acting area. Waxman draws back with the two girls

Terry That's two!

WHERE CAN THE NEXT ONE BE? (SONG)   5

Jack We found Number Two on a candy stall.
In the neat disguise of an aniseed ball.
We found Number One in a place so strange
In a bull's-eye, centre of a rifle range.
Now there's one more thing that's puzzling me—
Where can the next one be—be—be?
Where can the next one be?
Terry (*as they move off*) Let's keep looking!

Jack and Terry exit

Waxman (*thinking desperately*) Pearls! Eight black pearls! (*He stops suddenly*) I understand now. That little pig must be poisoned! (*He has an idea*) Where's the floss?
Floss Here I am!
Waxman (*annoyed*) *Candy floss!* Poisonous, petrifying candy floss!
Brunhilda (*rushing away*) I'll get it, Professor.

Brunhilda exits

Waxman That boy mustn't find any more pearls in the Fairground. Do you hear?
Floss (*suspiciously*) Why?
Waxman (*furiously*) Because I said so—that's why!
Floss Why don't you just waxify him, then?
Waxman I've changed my mind. Who wants a heap of junk!
Floss Junk?

Terry and Jack come back

Waxman I've too many waxed-up little boys as it is. They're two a penny.
Terry I beg your pardon.
Waxman (*charmingly, for the benefit of Terry and Jack*) They're two a penny.

Waxman pushes Floss off

Terry What are?
Waxman Sticks of candy floss—two for a penny. But for *you*, they're free! A perfect give-away!

Jack (*suspiciously*) There's a nasty taste somewhere.
Terry (*excitedly*) Come on, Jack. There's one for both of us.
Jack I don't want it.

Brunhilda enters with candy floss

Waxman There's only one anyway—a special one.

Brunhilda passes him one enormous stick of candy floss

You'll never taste anything like this.
Jack (*strongly*) No, Terry.
Terry Why not? What's the matter, Jack? You jealous? I'm enjoying myself in the Fairground. (*He takes the floss*)
Jack Give that to me!
Waxman (*to Jack*) Leave him alone. He can have what he wants.
Terry (*wrestling the floss from Jack*) Let go—you can't have it. It's mine!
(*He begins to eat it*) It's so sticky, tacky.

Waxman takes the floss out of Terry's hand and begins to wind it round Terry

Sweet Lady. (*Panicking*) I'm *stuck*. It's sticking to me. I can't get it off.
It's on my hand, in my eyes, in my hair—*Jack*! Don't just stand there.
Get it *off*!
Waxman (*hysterically chanting*) Sticky, gooey, treakly tack,
Tacky, gluey, ugly—wet!
Wait till you're covered from front to back,
Caught like a fly in Waxman's net!

Waxman, Brunhilda and Floss exit, giggling madly

Finally Jack manages to extricate Terry from the candy floss

Jack Keep still. Don't move.
Terry Ow! That hurt.
Jack It will for a moment.

Terry is completely freed

That's better.

Terry looks at Jack. Ashamed, Terry turns away

You were greedy—you forgot the pearls.
Terry It was that enormous stick of candy floss. I couldn't think of anything else, and then . . . What did she want to do that for?
Jack (*remembering*) "Caught like a fly in Waxman's net"—so it was *him*!
Terry (*his courage returning*) I'd like to meet Professor Waxman again, face to face! (*He sees Mr Barker, who has been playing the organ or watching all the adventures so far*)
Mr Barker Hello again. How's the Adventure of the Age?
Terry Not so bad, thank you. Seen any pearls?

Mr Barker (*mysteriously*) If you must find another clue—
 A metal hand will work for you.

*Two actors with large, metal, claw-like hands run in. They join each other
and represent a mechanical grab machine*

Terry A metal hand—
Jack A machine—
Mr Barker A *grab* machine.
Jack Watch out, Terry. Don't let it grab you!
Grab Machine Grab, grab, grab, GRAB!
Terry (*seeing something in one of the claw-like hands*) Look! Another pearl!
 How can we get it?
Jack (*approaching it*) It's inside the machine, we'll have to work the
 grab.
Grab Machine Click the lever close beside you,
 Try your luck and take a chance.
 You might claim our closest secret.
 Watch our clamping claws in dance!

Jack begins to operate the controls

 Grrrrrrrrrrrrrrrrrrr . . .
Terry Carefully, Jack. Go carefully.

Jack tries to "grab" the pearl by working the machine

Grab Machine Grrrrrrrrrrrrrrrrrrr . . .

The hand misses the pearl. Jack works the handles again

Terry Steady. Steady now.

Grab Machine Grrrrrrrrrrrrrrrrrrr . . .

*The hand misses again. Jack tries again and finally operates the machine
successfully*

Terry Got it! We've got it!
Grab Machine Grab, grab, grab, grab, *grab*! (*The two actors separate and
 make wild grabbing movements at Terry and the Audience*)

Jack and Terry run round, dodging the Grab Machine

Jack The machine! It's about to explode! Take cover!

 The Grab Machine exits. Stillness

Terry Whew! That was a near one. Three pearls now. Number Three.
 Put this one in a box. Now—find someone strong, Jack. This is a
 special pearl—we were nearly grabbed, trying to get this one.

*Jack takes another box from the usual stall, puts the pearl in it and gives it
to one of the Audience. He runs back to Terry*

That's three!

WHERE CAN THE NEXT ONE BE? (SONG)   **6**

Jack We found number three, as you all have seen,
      In the curling clutches of the Grab Machine,
      We found Number Two in a candy stall
      In the neat disguise of an aniseed ball.
      We found Number One in a place so strange,
      In a bull's-eye, centre of a rifle range.
      Now there's one more thing that's puzzling me—
      Where can the next one be—be—be?
      Where can the next one be?

Terry Now we're really on our way. Nothing can set us back now, not
even Professor Waxman.

Waxman suddenly appears with Brunhilda and Floss

Waxman That's what you think, my boy. Three pearls, is it?
Brunhilda I saw who's looking after them!
Waxman You've got friends, have you? Well, just you wait till I get my
Waxifier!
Floss (*horrified*) Oh, Professor Waxman, you can't waxify the children!

Waxman, Brunhilda and Floss exit

Jack Quick! Terry! Collect that pearl over there. (*He points to one of the
children looking after the pearls*)
Terry Why?
Jack (*to the same child*) Give your pearl back to Terry, please. And I'll
collect the other two.

They collect the pearls

Thank you. We'll move the pearls to the boys and girls over here. (*To
Terry*) You look out for him. Tell us when he's coming back. (*He takes
the pearls in their boxes to three other children in the rear of the auditorium*)
Terry (*peeping round the scenery*) Hurry, Jack! Don't be long. I can hear
his footsteps—I think he's coming; I can see his Waxifier.
Jack (*from the auditorium*) Terry, hide! Don't let him see you!

Terry hides

And the three who had the pearls before, don't worry—Waxman won't
touch you—now.

*Waxman returns with the Waxifier, followed by Brunhilda and Floss. Jack
hides near Terry*

Waxman Now! (*Looking around*) To waxify those three children. What
could they be in my waxworks?

Floss (*sweetly*) The three little kittens what lost their mittens.
Brunhilda No, that's soppy! The three little pigs!
Waxman That's better . . . Where are they?
Brunhilda (*pointing*) There!
Floss (*pointing*) There!
Waxman And over there!

The three move out into the auditorium

Now where are those pearls?

After a while they realize that the pearls have been moved

Brunhilda (*to Floss*) Have you got yours?
Floss No. Have you got yours?
Brunhilda No. Professor, have you got your pearl?
Waxman (*irritated*) No! Have you got yours?
Brunhilda ⎱ (*frightened*) No! (*Speaking together*)
Floss ⎰
Waxman I can't understand it. (*Referring to the Audience*) They're cunning, this lot.

They leave the auditorium, and return to the acting area

We must plot secret plans. Espionage!
Floss Pardon?
Brunhilda Secret Service!
Floss Pardon.
Waxman (*furiously*) SPY!
Brunhilda Can we disguise ourselves, too?
Floss (*excitedly*) Dress up! Ooooooooooh. Could we be pretty princesses?
Brunhilda (*disgusted*) Sickening! I'd like to be a general in charge of an army—all my buttons blazing! (*She is quite carried away*)
Waxman Sssssssssssssssh! Don't give away secrets—in war time! (*He glares at the Audience*) Return to camp!

Waxman exits

Brunhilda (*unable to leave the glory of the military*) Quuuuuuuuuick march!
Left, right, left, right.

Brunhilda hustles Floss off

Terry and Jack jump back on again

Terry Thanks for being so brave, and thank you for guarding the pearls.
Where are we now?
Mr Barker (*in a whisper*) Outside the Temple of the Mystic East!
Terry (*politely*) I beg your pardon.
Jack Did you say something?
Mr Barker (*still in a whisper*) My voice is tired. Listen:

Come this way, see the Eastern girls,
Dressed in silks and satins and pearls.

Terry Pearls? (*He points to Mr Barker*) Your tiepin! There's a black pearl set in it. That was quick, wasn't it, Mr Barker? What would you swop it for? (*Searching in his pocket*) I've a couple of caterpillars in a matchbox somewhere!

Jack (*pulling a petrol funnel from his own pocket*) What about this?

Mr Barker That's a better idea.

Terry (*scornfully*) That's Jack's petrol funnel.

Mr Barker It may be, but it'll make a super megaphone. No more tired voices now. 'Ere's the tiepin then. (*Handing it over*) Right, 'ere we go. Listen.

Terry Wait a minute, Mr Barker. (*Popping the pearl into a box, and handing it over to Jack*) Jack has to find someone to look after this pearl. Try over there this time, Jack.

Jack (*giving the box to a child*) Thank you. (*He runs back to Terry*)

Terry Now we've found four!

WHERE CAN THE NEXT ONE BE? (SONG)   7

Jack We found Number Four though we don't know why.
It was firmly planted in the Barker's tie.
We found Number Three, as you all have seen,
In the curling clutches of the Grab Machine.
We found Number Two on a candy stall
In the neat disguise of an aniseed ball.
We found Number One in a place so strange,
In a bull's-eye, centre of a rifle range.
Now there's one more thing that's puzzling me—
Where can the next one be—be—be?
Where can the next one be.

Terry All right, Mr Barker, what were you going to show us?

Mr Barker Ready?

Terry Yes.

Mr Barker Sure?

Jack Of course.

Mr Barker (*with a great roar through the petrol funnel megaphone*)
Come this way, see the Eastern girls,
Dressed in silks and satins and *pearls*!

Eastern music

Brunhilda and Floss enter, disguised as dancing girls

Terry Jack! Look what they've dragged up for Eastern girls! It's Floss and Brunhilda!

Jack Careful. (*Speaking quietly to Terry*) Professor Waxman has sent them to spy on us. Pretend you haven't noticed their disguise.

They sit and watch the "dancing girls"

Brunhilda (*dancing away*) I wonder what will happen, Floss, If I start getting fatter?

Terry (*calling out*) Well, lady, with a face like yours it doesn't really matter!

Floss (*to Terry*) She won a beauty contest, dear, so don't be such a tease.

Terry The only contest she could win is one for knobbly knees!

Brunhilda (*trying to keep up her dignity*)
You really are a nasty child, so cheeky to us girls.

Terry Well, if you want us to be friends you'll help us find the pearls!

Brunhilda (*losing her Eastern character for a moment*) You've a hope, you little——

Floss (*cutting in*) Brunhilda, keep your disguise up.

Brunhilda hitches up her costume

The girls exit to sinuous music through a "Mystic East" cut-out

Terry Come on, Jack. They might lead us to some more pearls—by mistake. We'll be all right together. (*He laughs*)

Jack (*seriously*) Just keep an eye open for Waxman, that's all.

Terry and Jack follow

The "Mystic East" cut-out might be reversed now—showing the interior of the Temple

Brunhilda and Floss enter through it

Brunhilda (*finding it all too much*) Floss! Are they coming inside?

Floss (*looking behind*) I think so, Brunhilda.

Brunhilda They'd better be. (*Rather worried*) The Professor's orders were to tempt them into the Temple.

Floss (*in her element*) Isn't this lovely? I like dancing.

Brunhilda I don't. I feel a right lollipop! (*Accidentally she touches Floss*)

Floss (*giggling*) Stop it—you're tickling me! I can't *bear* being tickled! I go to pieces if I'm tickled!

Terry and Jack enter

Terry There they are. Hey, that ring on Floss's hand. It's got a black pearl set in it! (*To Floss, who has put the ring behind her*) I'll swop you something for your pearl ring.

Brunhilda (*to Floss*) The Professor will kill you if he finds out.

Floss (*in a panic*) What shall I do? (*She has an idea*) It's yours if you can get it—out of the Snake Pit.

An actor representing the Snake enters

Floss throws the ring to the actor, who catches it. One of his arms, suitably costumed, becomes the Snake

Jack Watch yourself, Terry. It's a venomous viper.

A mysterious figure in Eastern costume enters

Terry (*to the mysterious figure*) Snakecharmer, please make the snake dance for you.

The Snakecharmer obliges with a few notes on his pipe

Now, Jack, there's your chance! Show us how it's done!

Nervously Jack approaches the Snake. The Snake lunges at him—Jack leaps back

You're doing fine, Jack—don't give up.

Jack tries again—the Snake darts at him

Please—try again.

Jack finally gets the ring away from the snake

Hurray! (*Getting hold of Jack*) That's five pearls we've got.
Jack There's another pearl somewhere—I can *smell* it! Mr Barker, have you any ideas?
Mr Barker Not a thing in my head.

The Indian God enters

Jack (*looking round*) No, but he has! The Indian God!
See, there's a black pearl set in his head-dress.

The arms of the Indian God begin to move

Jack This one's a problem.

Jack and Terry move closer to the God

Floss (*to Brunhilda*) I don't know what Professor Waxman will say about all this.
Brunhilda He'll waxify the whole lot if they're not careful! We'd better find him.
Floss (*to Snakecharmer*) Excuse me, have you seen Professor Waxman?
Snakecharmer (*removing part of his disguise*) I *am* Professor Waxman!
Floss Ohhhhhhhhhhhhhhh!
Brunhilda (*recovering from the shock*) Jolly good to see you, Professor. We've got so much to report.
Waxman I saw it all. (*Falling on his knees*) And I shall appeal to the Gods!

Floss and Brunhilda fall on their knees. Waxman directs his prayers to the Indian God

Eastern God from distant lands,
Squash them with your many hands.

A Sacrifice to squelch and squeeze
I offer you on bended knees!

The Indian God moves forward—Jack and Terry step back

Jack This one's too dangerous.
Terry I don't care. I must get that pearl.
Waxman (*to Brunhilda*) Go and help the Indian God.
Brunhilda (*to Floss*) We're to give him a hand. (*She demonstrates Indian dancing movements*)
Floss All right, but you mustn't tickle.
Terry What are they doing?

Brunhilda waves her arms in Eastern fashion

Jack Wait and see.
Floss All right—but you mustn't tickle!

Floss and Brunhilda stand behind the Eastern God and help him with arm-waving effect

Terry (*handing the pearl to Jack*) Here. Look after the fifth pearl. I'll get the sixth.
Jack (*as Terry approaches the God*) Terry! Come back!
Terry (*pulling the pearl from the God's forehead*) Got it!

All six arms trap him

Ahhhhhhhhhh! *Jack!*
Jack (*helpless, for the moment*) What can I do? An idea! I'll see if it works! (*He pulls a feather duster from a pocket*)
Floss (*seeing Jack advance with the feather duster*) No, not that! Anything but that!

Jack tickles the Indian God and his assistants. Terry is released

The Indian God, Brunhilda and Floss exit in hysterics, followed by the Snake

Waxman (*in a tremendous rage*) I'd like to tickle that boy with a *DAGGER*!

Waxman sweeps off in anger

Terry Jack what would I have done without you! We got the pearls though.
Jack Here's the fifth.
Terry And here's the sixth.
Jack (*to the Audience*) Who'll look after these?

Jack and Terry put the pearls in their boxes and hand them out to members of the Audience

Jack There! Don't forget, they're *precious*!
Terry Don't lose them.

WHERE CAN THE NEXT ONE BE? (SONG)   8

Jack We found Number Five on Floss's hand,
And the Sixth in the God from the Eastern land.
We found Number Four though we don't know why:
It was firmly planted in the Barker's tie.
We won Number Three as you all have seen
From the curling clutches of the Grab Machine.
We found Number Two on a candy stall
In the neat disguise of an aniseed ball.
We found Number One in a place so strange—
In a Bull's-eye, centre of a rifle range.
Now there's one more thing that's puzzling me—
Where can the next one be—be—be?
Where can the next one be?

Floss and Brunhilda rush on. They have seen where all the pearls are

Brunhilda We saw. We know where all the pearls are. (*To Floss*) We'll split on them.

Brunhilda attempts to rush off

Floss (*confused*) We're going to *SPLIT*!

Floss is pulled off by Brunhilda

Jack (*to the Audience*) Quick, take the pearls somewhere else, before Waxman comes back. If you have one of the pearls, get up out of your seat and give them as far away from you as possible. That's it—get up and take them to another place.

Movement among the Audience

Right! Now back to your seats. Hold the pearls up when I call your number one, two, three, four, five, six.

As he calls each number a child is shown holding up his/her pearl

Only two to go . . .
Terry Before we prove Tall Tom's innocence.
Jack Come on, Terry, let's hide.

Jack and Terry hide in the auditorium

Waxman enters with Brunhilda and Floss

Brunhilda Don't you want to know where the pearls are, Professor?
Waxman (*taking no notice*) That boy's gone far enough. I want him *squashed*!
Brunhilda But the pearls!

Waxman (*exasperated*) Six pearls are no good—they need *eight*! And they won't find the other two—I'll see to that.

Brunhilda (*fussing*) Don't frown like that. You'll get wrinkles.

Waxman From now on—it's a test of strength. (*He moves to the Test-Your-Strength machine*)

Floss But you're so strong—you're bound to win!

Waxman (*flexing his muscles*) Now for the hammer. (*He tries to lift the hammer from the Test-Your-Strength Machine*)

Brunhilda You've got lovely muscles. Perhaps you could drop that on the little boy's toes?

Floss Oh *no*!

Waxman (*to Floss, nastily*) Do you doubt that I'm strong?

Floss (*pathetically*) No! You're the "Strongest Man in the World"!

THE STRONG-MAN'S SONG (SONG)   **9**

Waxman builds up a relationship with the Audience. He moves among them—often "improvising" during the number

Waxman *Chorus:*
> Have you ever seen a man
> Quite as strong as me?
> I'm as brave as a lion
> I'm as tough as a tree,
> And I chew on bars of iron
> For my dinner, lunch and tea . . .
> That's me—
>   The big Strong Man.
> *Verse:*
> For fun I find a mountain
> Far too big for me.
> I tie around a rope
> And drag it to the sea.
> Or if I'm feeling extra tough,
> I take a breath then blow and puff,
> There comes-a-rippling in the ground
>   And houses all come tumbling down.

> *Chorus*

> *Verse:*
> So no-one causes trouble
> When they hear my name,
> And if they know what's good
> For them they'll run away
> 'Cos I'll bash 'em up until they cry,
> Then with my gun I'll waxify.
> There's no man yet that's beaten me
> My muscles are too big, you see.

> *Chorus* (*clapping*) "Olé!"

Waxman falls to the ground—exhausted. As the song ends, Terry and Jack come out of hiding

Machine Ring the bell and win a prize.
  You might get a big surprise!
Terry A "Test-Your-Strength" Machine. I'm ready for anything. The prize might be a pearl. (*He moves towards the machine*)
Jack (*seeing Waxman, holding Terry back*) Hold on. It's Waxman.
Terry I'm not afraid. Now we've met him face to face, we'll see who's the stronger. (*Running up to Waxman*) Let me try.
Waxman (*charmingly*) Of course. (*He manages to pass the hammer to Terry*)
Brunhilda (*excitedly*) He *will*—he'll drop it on the boy's toes!

Waxman drops the hammer, but misses Terry's toes. Terry hits the machine, but not very hard—sound effect. The indicator of the machine rises a little

Floss Not very good.
Terry I'm just getting the hang of it.

Terry tries again—another sound effect. The indicator rises more

Waxman (*sneering*) Not good enough. (*He laughs*)
Terry Please, Jack. Help me lift the hammer.

Jack helps Terry

Waxman That's not fair!

Terry and Jack bring the hammer down smartly—sound effect. The indicator reaches the height of the bell

Terry There! We've done it!
Waxman⎤
Brunhilda ⎬ *No!* (*Speaking together*)
Floss ⎦
Brunhilda The bell—it didn't ring.
Floss (*sympathetically*) You're too weak!
Terry But I did hit it! (*Appealing to the Audience*) Didn't I, everyone?
Waxman It didn't ring, so there!
Terry (*to Jack*) Let's look for another pearl—we can't have been as strong as we thought.
Jack Wait. (*He inspects the top of the machine*)
Brunhilda There's something up there.

Jack pulls something out of the machine

Floss What is it?
Waxman What's he got?
Brunhilda A lump of grit.
Floss A pebble.
Jack No. It's a *pearl*!

Terry A black pearl! That's why the bell didn't ring. SEVEN pearls!
Waxman Curse the wretches! (*He moves away into a corner*)
Floss ⎫
Brunhilda ⎬ Professor, wait for us. (*Speaking together*)

Waxman goes into a huddle with Floss and Brunhilda

Jack goes to the usual stall and gets another box

Jack (*quickly handing out the pearl in its box to someone in the Audience*)
Please look after the seventh pearl.
Terry Wow! Seven pearls!

WHERE CAN THE NEXT ONE BE? (SONG)   10

Jack We found Number Seven when the bell went wrong:
It was under the bit which went "ding dong".
We found Number Five on Floss's hand
And the Sixth in the God from the Eastern land.
We found Number Four though we don't know why:
It was firmly planted in the Barker's tie
We found Number Three, as you all have seen,
In the curling clutches of the Grab Machine.
We found Number Two on a candy stall
In the neat disguise of an aniseed ball.
We found Number One in a place so strange,
In a bull's-eye, centre of a rifle range.
Now there's one more thing that's puzzling me—
Where can the last one be—be—be?
Where can the last one be?
Terry Only one more pearl to find, and then we'll know the truth, Jack.
Jack We must be close to the last one. (*He wanders away*)
Waxman (*coming out of the huddle and speaking to Terry*) As you're so
strong, my boy—(*greasily*)—will you help me? Your friend helps *you*—
it's only fair.

*Terry looks dubious. Waxman moves back to the "Test-Your-Strength"
machine*

If you could just hold the toes of the machine while I have a go—you
hit it so hard you've made it wobbly.

*Terry bends down to steady the place where the hammer will hit the machine.
Waxman turns to Brunhilda and Floss*

Come on, you two—help me. Now close your eyes in case I make the
dust fly.

*Jack returns, and sees what is happening. Waxman, Brunhilda and Floss are
about to bring the hammer down on Terry's head*

Jack No! Terry, get up! (*He grabs hold of him*) Let's get out of this.

Terry and Jack run off

Waxman (*with the hammer still poised*) No! Come back. (*To the other two*) Don't push. (*Calling after Terry and Jack*) I want to . . .

Brunhilda and Floss bring down the hammer on to Waxman's toes

Aghhhhhhhhhh! You *idiots*! I'll waxify you. I'll waxify *everyone*!

With a sudden burst of strength Waxman chases Brunhilda and Floss out with the hammer. Terry and Jack peep round the scenery

Terry He's gone. Isn't he a mess!

Jack and Terry enter

Jack (*seriously*) He's a monster!
Terry He couldn't knock spots off a rice pudding!
Jack (*wondering*) He really doesn't want us to find the last pearl, does he?
Terry Well, we have seven—we've nearly done it.
Jack Only one to go.
Terry Tall Tom must have been innocent, mustn't he?
Jack We can't *prove* it—not until we have all the eight pearls.
Terry He's *got* to be innocent. (*Wondering*) But if he was, who *did* steal the necklace?

Quiet, slightly sinister music   **11**

The Man of Mystery enters

I wish we knew more about Tall Tom. I wish we knew more about the Fantastic Fairground, and how it all began.

Terry and Jack come close to the mysterious figure in the black cloak

Man of Mystery (*slowly and deliberately*) I am the Man of Mystery. I look into the Past. Come, we will look into my crystal.

They gather round a crystal ball—it grows darker

Do not move. See. The crystal is clouding over. We are reaching into the Past.
Terry Look, Jack.
Man of Mystery Do not speak. We are in the Past—the Middle Ages, when the Fair began.

Actors begin to re-enact what is in the crystal. A Medieval Lady comes on. Waxman, in medieval costume, follows

Terry There's Waxman. He must have lived in the Middle Ages.

Waxman steals a purse from the Lady, who does not notice   **11a**

Waxman and the Medieval Lady exit

(*Indignantly*) He stole that lady's purse!
Man of Mystery Be still The crystal changes. But we are still in the Past—when Elizabeth the First was Queen.

An Elizabethan Lady comes on. Waxman, in Elizabethan costume, follows

Terry (*excitedly*) Waxman's there again.

Waxman stealthily slides a ring from the Lady's hand. She does not notice

He stole that lady's ring!

The Elizabethan Lady and Waxman exit

Man of Mystery The crystal is faint, and the images will disappear if you do not concentrate. Concentrate. Ah, it begins to happen. We are **11b** still in the Past, but not so far away now. Just two hundred years ago.
Terry Two hundred years ago. That's when the Highwayman was living.

Lady Melanie and her Maid enter, followed by Waxman in eighteenth-century costume

Jack There's the Lady Melanie.
Terry And Waxman! (*Horrified*) He must always have been alive!
Jack He's seen the necklace—the black pearl necklace.

Tall Tom enters

Terry Look. There's the Highwayman, Tall Tom.
Man of Mystery Be quiet. The picture will fade. We must make it live again. (*Almost in a trance*) Who has stolen the Lady Melanie's pearl necklace?

Waxman steals the necklace with a big, dramatic gesture—only Terry and Jack see it

Terry The Professor! The Professor Waxman!
Waxman (*after pocketing the necklace*) Tall Tom has. (*He points accusingly at him*) He is guilty, and must be hanged!

The figures of the crystal go off, together with Waxman; so does the Man of Mystery

Terry But he wasn't guilty. We saw it—Professor Waxman stole the pearls. He must have hidden them in the Fairground. (*Looking round*) Man of Mystery . . .

Jack He's gone.

Terry (*realizing*) Oh, Jack. Professor Waxman has lived for hundreds and hundreds of years.

Waxman suddenly appears, back in his usual costume

Waxman (*quite terrifyingly*) I have lived since time began. And no-one, not even you or your friend Jack, will stop me. (*To the Audience*) And as for you! I know who's got those seven pearls. They're over there—(*he points*)—and there, and there, and there. There, there, there! I'll have them off you before you're much older. You just wait and see.

Waxman exits. Stillness

Terry It's too much. I'm tired. Let's have a rest.

Jack Right. (*To the Audience*) We'll have a break before we look for the eighth pearl.

Terry But Professor Waxman will steal the pearls from the boys and girls.

Jack No, he won't. We'll pass the pearls on again. (*To the Audience*) If you have one of the seven pearls, pass it on to someone else during the Interval. Take your time before you decide . . .

Terry But don't lose them.

Jack Give them to someone you've never met before.

Terry Have you got that? See you soon.

Jack and Terry exit

Mr Barker But there's one more thing that's puzzling me—
Where can the last one be, be—be,
Where can the *last* one be?

INTERVAL

ACT II

Mr Barker comes on. He plays the Entracte

Mr Barker Hello again, boys and girls. Welcome back to the FANTASTIC FAIRGROUND. Remember?

ROLL UP, ROLL UP (SONG)   **12**

> Come roll up and join the fun
> Sing along—The Fair's begun.

Repeat the chorus until the Audience is involved

Continuing the Adventure of the Age . . . You remember that Terry, together with his friend Jack of All Trades, is searching in the Fantastic Fairground for the eight black pearls which made up the lady Melanie's necklace.

Terry and Jack come on

Terry So far we've got seven.
Jack (*to the Audience*) Call out and hold it up if you've got pearl number one, two, three, four, five, six or seven.

The Audience do so

Good, they're all here.
Terry The last pearl will be the most difficult, I know.
Jack You should feel better after your rest.
Terry Let's start looking then.
Jack Right, this way.

They wander off

Mr Barker (*to the Audience*) If Terry and Jack collect all eight of the black pearls, they will prove that Tall Tom did not steal them two hundred years ago, and that Professor Waxman—Master of Disguise—did!

Waxman, disguised as an Ice-Cream Man, enters

ICE-CREAM SONG (SONG)   **12 [cont.]**

Waxman (*chorus*) The kids all around will shout and scream,
          "What do we like?—We like ice-cream!"

Brunhilda and Floss, also suitably disguised, enter. They follow Waxman to the Sweet and Ice-cream Stall

Floss Doesn't the Professor look smart?

Brunhilda Turn himself to anything he can. Genius, sheer genius.

Floss Who would have thought that he could *transpose* himself into a . . .

Brunhilda (*looking closely*) Baker!

Waxman (*annoyed*) I'm an Ice-Cream Man!

Brunhilda (*to Floss*) There you see—you were wrong!

Waxman Don't forget we're here to *poison* . . .!

They whisper together

Floss You mustn't—he'll have tummyache.

Waxman Ssssh! (*Referring to the Audience*) They'll hear you.

Brunhilda Leave it to me, Professor. (*Advancing forward, threateningly*) You won't say anything, will you?

Floss Perhaps if we sang them a song, they'd promise not to tell.

Waxman (*feeling his authority is lost*) What!

ICE-CREAM SONG (SONG)   12 [cont.]

Floss (*timidly*) Only if you want to as well, Professor.

Waxman ⎰ Guess what I've got in store for you.
Brunhilda ⎱ A penny for one and a tuppence for two,
Floss ⎰ Coloured all pink and white and green—
Fluffy great clouds of fresh ice-cream.
The kids all around will shout and scream,
"What do we like? We like ice-cream!"

Brunhilda 'Operatic you are, Professor—'operatic!

Waxman I suppose the boys and girls could join in the chorus—(*nastily*)—but they'd never remember the words.

Brunhilda No, they wouldn't remember!

Floss I think they could.

Brunhilda Pooh! *You* couldn't remember it!

Floss Yes I can. (*Thinking very hard*) "The kids all round will shout and scream, "What do we like? We—like—(*faltering*)—ice-cream?"

Waxman Huh! Well! *They'll* never be able to, so there!

How would you like a strawberry ice?
A wafer maybe or a cornet is nice,
Waxman Some of the stuff is plain, of course,
Brunhilda Rippled all through with "choklit" sauce.
Floss The kids all around will shout and scream,
"What do we like? We like ice-cream!"

Waxman See! I told you they wouldn't be able to!

Floss But they did. (*Appealing to the Audience*) Didn't you?

Brunhilda It must have been very quiet—I couldn't hear them.

Floss (*confidentially, to the Audience*) Make Professor Waxman jump out of his skin—sing extra loudly, after the next verse.

> Don't leave the Fair without a taste.
> On silly old things your money you'll waste.

Waxman Crying, you'll go to bed and dream
Brunhilda Of a pink and white and green ice-cream.
Floss The kids all around will shout and scream,
> "What do we like? We like ice-cream!"

Waxman I did hear someone *whisper* that time!
Floss But they've had their ice-cream, Professor. What about Terry? Which flavours have you got for him?
Waxman Bluebottles and bumblebees.
Brunhilda Octopus eyes, and earwigs.
Waxman Kipper and custard.
Brunhilda Ha, ha, ha, ha!

Jack and Terry enter

Waxman (*seeing Terry and Jack enter*) Shhhhhh! He's coming this way. (*Adjusting his disguise*) The show must go on. One more time.
> The kids all around will shout and scream,
> "What do we like?—We like ice-cream!"

They busy themselves round the Ice-cream Stall

Terry There's an ice-cream man. (*Terry moves towards Waxman*) Come on, let's . . .
Jack Look closer.
Terry Ooooooo—it's Waxman—up to his tricks again.
Jack (*pulling him away*) Right, off we go!
Terry Jack, the last pearl! The Professor might accidentally lead us to it.
Terry Not if we're careful!
Jack It's too dangerous.
Jack (*changing his mind*) Promise you won't taste any of his ice-cream! Play him along—I won't be far away. (*He hides*)
Waxman (*to Terry, with an excrutiating Italian accent*) You look a nice little boy. You're just in time for a special treat.
Brunhilda An extra special treat.
Floss Delicious ice-cream.
Brunhilda Extra delicious.
Terry (*politely*) I don't think I want one, thank you.
Waxman But all little boys like ice-cream—especially if it's free!
Brunhilda Extra large.
Floss Extra special.
Terry (*tempted*) How large?
Waxman (*demonstrating*) That big!
Terry (*impressed*) Ooooooooh! What flavours?
Waxman Any flavour in the world—ask, it's yours and more besides.
Terry (*imaginatively*) Strawberry ripple with nuts and extra cream and choclate sauce.
Jack (*jumping from his hideout*) Terry!

Terry (*quickly*) I've got a *plan*!

Jack hides, Terry addresses Waxman

And a *black cherry on the top*!
Waxman (*obliging*) There you are.

Terry grabs the ice-cream

Terry It's the last pearl.
Jack (*grabbing it*) No, it's not—it really *is* a black cherry! It's a trap!
Don't . . .

But Terry starts to lick the ice-cream

Terry! I told you!
Terry It's delicious . . . (*His face changes*) Oooh, the pain. (*Clutching his stomach*) Jack, help me! *Do* something!

Jack is helpless

Waxman Think of all that ice-cream with—cod liver oil.
Brunhilda Fatty fried bread!
Waxman Cold cabbage juice! Ha, ha, ha!
Brunhilda Victory at last, Professor. (*To Floss*) Leave the enemy to tend the wounded.
Floss We can't leave him like that. (*To Jack*) You'll have to get a doctor.

Dr Quack enters

Dr Quack Doctor! Who said "doctor"? Ladies and gentlemen, Dr Quack at your service! Guess how old I am!

Waxman, Brunhilda and Floss scuttle behind the stall

Old as the 'ills. I tell you—and look at that—(*jumping in the air*)—like a spring lamb. You know why? Daily doses of my own tonic! Cures everything. I've travelled the world, I 'ave, selling this, the 'ole world . . .
Jack Please.
Dr Quack What can I do for you, mate?
Jack Can you help him?
Terry Ahhhhhh—aw—oooooooo!
Dr Quack (*suddenly losing confidence*) Oh, well, this stuff's for "grown-ups" really—no good for little boys.
Jack (*to Dr Quack*) You're a cheat!
Terry Do something, please! My tummy!
Floss Go on, Dr Quack. Let's see if the stuff really works. (*To the Audience*) Ask Dr Quack to help him.

Floss is silenced by Brunhilda

Dr Quack 'Ope it doesn't make 'im worse! 'Ere you are, son, you try a drop of that. (*Opening a bottle and giving it to Terry*) Well. I'll just be off. There's some special 'erbs I need for a new recipe.

Terry drinks

Terry Ooooooo, awwwww. Hey, I'm better—that stuff's good. The pain's gone!
Jack Hurray!
Dr Quack (*who was just about to go*) Well now, as I was saying . . . This medicine will cure anything. It cures—what was wrong with you, sonny?
Terry Tummyache after poisoned ice-cream.
Dr Quack Yes—well—as you can see it cures tummyaches after poisoned ice-cream, septic knee, cauliflower ear. So come along, and get your bottles while stocks still last.
Waxman (*coming from behind the stall*) You're very clever.

Brunhilda and Floss come out after Waxman

Brunhilda Too clever.
Waxman We need a doctor—in the Waxwork Chamber!
Dr Quack Really!
Brunhilda Dr Jekyll . . .
Waxman And Mr Hyde! (*He shakes his wax spray*)
Dr Quack What do you mean? Waxworks?
Waxman Waxified!
Dr Quack Oh no! (*He tries to get away*)
Waxman (*squirting wax*) Quick—after Quack!

Waxman and Brunhilda run after Quack, and close in on him. There is a dreadful scream from Doctor Quack as he is waxified

Floss (*watching from the sidelines*) Oh dear. There's another one to dust.

Mournful music. The three villains take off their hats, before the new wax-work is slid off

(*To Terry and Jack*) Don't you get waxified. It's not worth it.
Waxman (*to Terry and Jack, as he exits*) You haven't heard the last of this.

Waxman goes

Brunhilda (*to Floss*) And you'll have to be disciplined.

USHERETTES' DUET (SONG)—*optional*   **13**

Brunhilda **Floss**	Professor Waxman's gone too far, He's got us in a stew. There are too many waxworks in the Chamber And much more work than two were meant to do. Isn't that true? Isn't that true?
Brunhilda	If I've told you fifteen thousand times It seems it's once too few,

	That yours is not to reason why,
	Yours is just to do what I tell you—
	Tell you to do. Has that got through?
Floss	Since you are so enlightened, and I'm really rather frightened
	Won't you tell me why you never help with cleaning meant for two?
Brunhilda	Because I am the Foreman, Chief Usherette and Doorman,
	And you're a weedy Junior, and rather stupid too.
Floss	I always knew, the same to you.
Brunhilda	I'll have no cheek, you little freak:
	I'll have your guts for garters.
	I'll have your ears for souvenirs,
	And feed your hair to a grizzly bear
	For starters. Your Tootsies too, I'll tickle them blue.
Floss	Brunhilda, please don't be angry, please don't be so cruel:
	Professor scares me, can't you see?
Brunhilda	I think he's rather keen on me.
	In fact I have a notion that I'm in for a promotion
	Any day. Anyway, he's the Boss, Floss.

Floss Brunhilda, listen. The Professor's potty!

Brunhilda There'll be no mutiny in my military! Attention, quick march

Brunhilda and Floss march off

Terry They're all mad.

Jack Poor Dr Quack!

Terry (*holding up the bottle*) I can recommend that bottle of medicine.

Jack We still haven't got that last pearl.

Terry We'll never find it.

Jack Don't give up hope. (*To the Audience*) That goes for you, too. Are you all still looking after the pearls? Good. Hold on to them tightly.

HAVE A LITTLE BIT OF HOPE (SONG)   14

When you find yourself in trouble . . .
And you don't think you can cope
Cross your fingers, cross your toes . . .
Have a little bit of hope . . .
Have a little bit of hope . . .
Find yourself a lucky clover
Keep it by you just in case . . .
You may need it come tomorrow
Then your troubles you can face!
When you find yourself in trouble
And you don't think you can cope
Cross your fingers, cross your toes
Have a little bit of hope . . .
Have a little bit of hope

Have a little bit of hope ...
Have a little bit of hope ...

Terry Something is going to happen. I can feel it.

Mathew, the Merry-Go-Round Man, enters. He is a kindly old man dressed in Victorian costume. He moves towards his Merry-Go-Round which can be simply suggested by maypole-type ribbons which are eventually attached to the horses

Mathew (*calling*) Esmerelda! Priscilla!
Jack Lovely day!
Mathew (*sadly*) Is it? I've lost them again.
Terry Who?
Mathew Priscilla—Esmeralda—my horses. It's time for the Merry-Go-Round, and there's nothing to go on it. I used to have horses and hens, lions and tigers, even dragons once—but that was a hundred years ago.
Terry A hundred years ago!
Mathew When Queen Victoria was on the throne, God bless her—(*calling into the distance*)—Esmeralda! Priscilla!
Terry (*whispering*) Jack, do you realize everyone in the Fantastic Fairground's really a ghost!
Mathew (*going on with his tale*) My Merry-Go-Round was the toast of all the fairs in England. Mathew Mudwinkle's Merry-Go-Round they called it. We travelled the country, toured the towns and villages, and then we came to this Common. After that, nothing seemed to go right. When the Fairground music began, fewer and fewer came running towards the Merry-Go-Round—and one day there was no-one, just the animals.
Terry Animals?
Mathew On the Merry-Go-Round. But no-one climbed on their backs and held on to the reins, so they ran away one by one.
Terry Maybe they were tired of riding round and round in circles—never getting anywhere—always coming back to the same place.
Jack (*defending Mathew*) Some people *want* to come back to the same place.
Terry But they don't get anywhere. They just go round and round.
Mathew So does the earth—round the sun.
Terry I want to go to the moon! Up and up! Take a ride on a rocket!
Mathew Not on my Merry-Go-Round you won't. (*Calling out again*) Priscilla! Esmeralda!

An old, dilapidated Merry-Go-Round Horse enters. Too tired to neigh, he nods his head wearily

Arthur! Poor old Arthur—I'd forgotten him.
Terry (*stroking him*) Isn't he beautiful?
Mathew Been for a gallop round the Fair, have you? You want your breakfast, eh? Sorry. I've nothing for you.

Terry (*searching his pocket*) I've a sweet somewhere . . . (*He finds one*) There! You're a lovely horse.

Mathew Old faithful, is Arthur. One of these days when I'm too old to turn the handle, I'll let him go—like the others. Thanks for coming back, Arthur. I'll paint your ears red tomorrow. (*He winds the handle— moving Arthur round*)

ROUNDABOUT (SONG)   14a

Mr Barker Hey, little boy, do you want a ride?
              Step in the stirrup and climb up high.
              Though you will stay here in the Fair
              Dream that you're travelling anywhere.
              You will go up, down, roundabout, roundabout.
              Never before have you felt so well—
              Up, down, roundabout, roundabout,
              Round—on our carousel.

Terry I must have a ride.

During the song, Mathew has been winding the handle of the Merry-Go-Round and Arthur has been moving round—but now he suddenly stops. Arthur collapses

Mathew Oh dear, we've broken down. Sorry, my boy. Arthur and I are very old. We need a new handle.

Jack No you don't. (*He inspects the damage*) You need oiling. (*Out of his pocket comes an oil can*) The Merry-Go-Round (*squirt*), Arthur (*squirt*), and you (*squirt*).

Mathew (*rejuvenated*) It's Mudwinkle's Mended Merry-Go-Round.

Terry Mudwinkle's *Modern* Merry-Go-Round.

Mathew (*thrilled*) You mean we'll be powered by steam?

Waxman suddenly appears, with Brunhilda and Floss disguised as two fairground horses who jump onto the Merry-Go-Round

Waxman By electricity! Don't lag behind the times, Mudwinkle!

Mathew (*seeing the horses*) It's Priscilla and Esmeralda—back again!

Terry jumps onto Arthur's back. Waxman takes hold of the Merry-Go-Round handle and turns it. The Merry-Go-Round begins to move

Jack It's not Priscilla *or* Esmeralda.

Terry (*as it begins to turn with Terry and Waxman on it*) It's Brunhilda and Floss.

ROUNDABOUT (SONG) *reprise*   14a

Waxman Come, little lad, take a ride with me.
           Visit the stars or heaven maybe
           Don't hold on and you'll find it fun.

Jack   Don't listen to him—just run, run, run.
Waxman   You will go up, down, roundabout, roundabout,
       Faster you'll go till you think you'll fly
       Up, down, roundabout, roundabout,
       Round—till you hit the sky!

Terry pulls something out of Arthur's head

Terry   Jack! I've found the pearl—the last one. It was here, on Arthur's *brow*!
Waxman   Right, you've asked for it.

Waxman works the handle faster. The horses whizz round

Mathew   My Merry-Go-Round's breaking up.
Floss   I've had enough!!!
Brunhilda (*surprisingly*) So've I!!

   Brunhilda and Floss jump off the Merry-Go-Round and gallop away

Waxman (*chasing them*) Come back, you horrible horses!

   Waxman exits waving the disconnected handle. The Merry-Go-Round slows down. Jack takes hold of Arthur

Jack   Steady there, Arthur. It's all right. It's all over.
Mathew (*stroking Arthur*) I'm here, Arthur. Don't fret yourself.

The broken-down Merry-Go-Round has finally stopped

Jack   All right, Terry?
Terry (*dusting himself down*) Just about. Here's the pearl! May we have it, Mr Mudwinkle? (*Matthew nods and the pearl is given to one of the audience*)
Mathew (*sadly*) No use to me now. Nor Arthur. You're all too fast for us. (*Taking hold of Arthur's reins*) Never mind, Arthur, stick your nose in the air: we're not beaten yet. (*He leads Arthur away*) We'll build a new merry-go-round with horses, hens, dragons . . .
Terry   Motor cars, aeroplanes and rocketships! All on Mudwinkle's Merry-Go-Round!
Mathew (*as he leads Arthur off*) With Arthur leading them all. Come on, old boy.

   Mathew and Arthur exit

Terry (*calling after them*) Thank you, Mr Mudwinkle, for helping us find the last pearl. (*He turns to Jack*) Jack, I can't believe it. All eight of the black pearls.
Jack (*to Audience*) Hold up your pearl in its box, when I call the number. One, two, three, four, five, six, seven, eight. Right. Bring your pearls out here to us.

The Eight Children are invited on to the acting area and give up their pearls.

They return to the auditorium. Jack and Terry arrange the pearls in numerical order. The letters on each fit together and are revealed to the Audience

Terry Look, Jack, they spell "Necklace"!

WHERE CAN THE NEXT ONE BE? (SONG)   15

Jack We found Number Eight on the Merry-Go-Round.
    Just a little more work, and we're homeward bound.
    We found Number Seven when the bell went wrong—
    It was under the bit which went "ding dong".
    We found Number Five on Floss's hand,
    And the Sixth in the God from the Eastern land.
    We found Number Four, though we don't know why—
    It was firmly planted in the Barker's tie.
    We found Number Three as you all have seen
    In the curling clutches of the Grab Machine.
    We found Number Two on a candy stall
    In the neat disguise of an aniseed ball.
    We found Number One in a place so strange—
    In a bulls-eye, centre of a rifle range.
    But there's one more thing that's bothering me—
    The end to the mystery . . .
    The end to the mystery!

Terry (*to the Audience*) Thanks for looking after the pearls. Now we've got all eight, we've proved that Tall Tom didn't steal the Lady Melanie's pearls.

Jack But the Adventure's not over yet.

The light begins to fade

The final episode of the Adventure of the Age is about to begin.

Terry We must catch Professor Waxman——

Jack —in his own den—the Waxwork Tent.

They move towards the Waxwork Tent

Jack Quick, hide. (*To the Audience*) Don't let anyone know we're here.

Mr Barker Take care, take care, take care!   **15** (*cont.*)
    Little boy, don't go down there.
    For that's where the villain and his helpers dwell,
    And what happens down there no-one lives to tell.
    Take care, take care, take care.

Brunhilda and Floss enter. They creep round the Tent and bump into each other

Brunhilda Who's that?
Floss What?
Brunhilda Who?

Floss Where?
Brunhilda Here.
Floss Oh.
Terry (*jumping up*) It's Brunhilda and Floss. Jack, where are you? (*He disappears behind a stall*)
Brunhilda Did you say something?
Floss No.
Brunhilda Who did then?
Floss (*peering into the auditorium*) I've a feeling we're being watched.
Brunhilda (*shuddering*) By Professor Waxman!
Floss Oh no. I hope not.
Brunhilda I've never seen him so angry.
Floss Big Bully!
Brunhilda I hated being a fairground horse!
Floss He'll waxify us all.
Brunhilda (*crying*) I don't want to go that way.
Floss (*looking round*) Which way?
Brunhilda Waxified! 'Ave everyone stare at you.
Floss They'd make faces, and you wouldn't be able to do them back.

Waxman enters quietly and creepily

Waxman (*menacingly*) What's all this? It's not "Closing Time". (*Peering into the auditorium*) There's still a few people out there in the Fairground. Call them in. And after they've looked at my waxworks—they can *become* my waxworks! Hee, hee, hee, hee. (*To Brunhilda and Floss*) Come on, get on with it! Call in the customers! I'll be listening—inside!

Waxman exits to the Waxwork Tent

Brunhilda and Floss take up their positions to call out to the Audience

Brunhilda (*trembling*) Step this way to the Waxwork Tent.
Floss (*quaking*) And see the most unusual set of waxworks this side of the moon.
Brunhilda If anyone's been nasty to you . . .
Floss Point 'em out, and we'll have them waxified!
Brunhilda Not just a wax copy. But the genuine thing—all waxed up!
Floss Waxified by Waxman's Waxifier. 'Ave them waxified!
Brunhilda Guaranteed to last hundreds and hundreds of years.

A figure with a torch moves through the darkness, it is Jack

   Ohhhhhh! It's a waxwork—de-waxified!
Floss Professor!

  Floss and Brunhilda rush off

Terry (*coming into the acting area, and recognizing the figure*) Jack! It's you.

Terry and Jack move towards the Waxwork Tent

Mr Barker Carefully, Terry, don't get caught, slip out quick and run,
  Terrible things may happen here, things to hide from, things to fear
  Deep, dark secrets, ages old, kept by the wicked one.

Scenery change—to inside the Waxwork Tent

Jack (*to the Audience*) Shhhhhh! We're inside. We're all inside the Wax-
  work Tent.
Terry It's so dark and cold.
Jack Look. Waxworks.
Terry (*finding the odd limb*) Legs and arms—made of wax.
Jack All the people the Professor has waxified . . .
Terry In bits and pieces.
Jack (*discovering something*) Here's Dr Quack's hat.
Terry (*bumping into another figure*) Ohhhhhh! (*He turns*) It's the Highway-
  man.

*They inspect the impressive waxwork, actually represented by the actor who
played Tall Tom previously*

Jack Tall Tom!
Terry I thought he was hanged!
Jack (*touching him*) No. He's been waxified, too.

Jack switches on his torch

Terry Jack, what are you doing? Put that torch away. If the Professor . . .

*Jack shines his torch, which casts a strangely coloured glow, on to Tall
Tom's face and body. Strange, tingling music*

  It's fantastic. You're melting him. He's coming alive again . . .

*Tall Tom slowly moves—he shakes his head—then stretches his whole body
as though coming awake*

  Tall Tom, you're innocent. We found all the lady Melanie's pearls and
  we've proved it. And what's more, we found out who did steal them—it
  was Professor Waxman!
Tall Tom (*still a bit stiff*) Waxman? (*Remembering*) Waxman! He kid-
  napped me and . . .
Jack Waxified you!
Tall Tom (*looking at the Audience*) Who are these people?
Terry Friends of ours. They've helped us.
Waxman (*off*) Search the Tent!
Terry (*terrified*) What will we do now?
Tall Tom Don't worry. A highwayman is used to ambush. (*To the Audience*)
  Pretend to be waxworks. Boys and girls, stand up or sit down, whatever
  you like, use your body in all kinds of different ways, only pretend to be
  waxworks.

*Movement in the auditorium. Jack and Terry guide and help the Audience
and pretend to be waxworks as well*

Listen. Wait for my signal!

Tom demonstrates an arm gesture

> And then all aim at Professor Waxman and say the words: "Waxman, you are a villain, and a thief!" Now, I want you all to point at Waxman and say those words when I give you the signal. Now . . .! (*He encourages the Audience to try it*) Good. Be waxworks and be still, and don't forget to wait for my signal. Shh . . .

> *When the Audience and Actors are still, Waxman, Brunhilda and Floss enter. The girls shining their torches*

Waxman What happened? Where is this monster?

Brunhilda It must be somewhere, Professor.

Floss (*pointing her torch*) Look at all these waxworks.

Waxman (*looking around*) I can't believe it. (*Moving to the auditorium*) You have done well. (*He wanders among the waxworks*) I don't remember waxifying all these. The Chamber of Little Horrors! (*To some unsuspecting adults*) Some of them look a bit mouldy, I know; they need melting down a peg or two. Please don't touch the waxworks, you don't know where they've been. (*And so on, until he returns to the acting area*) What's this! (*Angrily*) It's the boy and his friend. But they haven't been waxified —(*realizing the trap*)—yet!

Tall Tom (*repeating the signal gesture*) Waxman! You are a villain and a thief!

Everyone joins in

> (*Alone*) It was you who stole the Lady Melanie's pearls. Give yourself up to JUSTICE!

Waxman (*panicking and rushing wildly around*) Tall Tom! Curse you.

Jack Don't be frightened, anyone. Sit down in your seats.

The Audience does so

Jack and Tall Tom move slowly towards Waxman

Waxman Pearls nothing! What's the good of proof if you can't catch me? *No-one* will catch me. I shall go on for ever and ever and ever.

> *Waxman rushes out*

Brunhilda
Floss } Professor, wait for us. (*Speaking together*)

> *Brunhilda and Floss chase Waxman off. Another of the Actors enters. He becomes Master of the Chase, dressed in Victorian hunting gear*

CHASE CHANT

Master of the Chase After him, after him! Don't let him go!

Tall Tom Find the rogue, find the rogue
  My innocence to show.

They search the Fairground

Terry Where is he now? Where is he now?
  As quiet as a mouse
Tall Tom Where is the rogue? Where is the rogue?
Master of the Chase He's in the Haunted House.

Waxman, Brunhilda and Floss hide. The Haunted House might best be suggested by a lighting projection

Jack We know you're in there, Waxman, you won't get away.
Waxman (*off*) That's what you think, Jack of All Trades. I'll waxify you, just as I waxified Tall Tom for two hundred years.
Tall Tom (*to the Audience*) Listen, everyone. Can you frighten Waxman out of the Haunted House?
Terry How? What can we do?
Tall Tom Make noises you'd hear in the Haunted House! Groans, grunts, Creaks and whispers.
Terry Moans, sighs—and screams!
Jack Ghost noises, bat noises . . .
Tall Tom The wind in the chimney. Ready, everyone? Wait for my signal to begin, and to stop! (*He demonstrates appropriate arm movements*) Ready, go!

Haunted house noises from the Audience. Brunhilda and Floss rush about, terrified. Waxman escapes, they follow him. Scenery change

CHASE CHANT

Master of the Chase We've got the proof, we've got the proof.
Terry We found the final clue.
Master of the Chase You're in a cage, you're in a cage, imprisoned in the Zoo!

Waxman, Brunhilda and Floss are seen hidden once more. The "Zoo" could be another lighting projection

Jack Come on, Waxman. We know you're there—among the animals!
Tall Tom (*cocking his pistol*) Come on out, Waxman, with hands raised above your head.

Two trembling figures emerge

Terry It's Floss and Brunhilda!
Brunhilda (*terrified*) You can do what you like to us—we don't care!
Floss Only please don't tickle us!

Brunhilda and Floss surrender willingly

Tall Tom It's Waxman we want. He's still in there, in the Zoo. (*To the Audience*) Make all the animal noises you can think of. Lions—

Terry Tigers—
Jack Parrots—
Master of the Chase Elephants—
Brunhilda Ostriches—
Floss And tortoises!
Tall Tom Wait for my signal to start—and stop! (*Again the appropriate signals are demonstrated*) Now!

Animal noises from the Audience

Waxman rushes out. The others chase after him and exit. Scenery change

CHASE CHANT

Master of the Chase (*as they go off*) Chase him here, chase him there,
Waxman, run aground.
Chase him up, chase him down,
Until the wretch is found.

Terry returns, he is lost

Terry Jack, where are you?
I'm dizzy, in a daze!

Waxman enters with his Waxifier

Waxman I've got you now, I've got you now,
I've trapped you in the maze!

The "Maze" might be another lighting projection. Waxman advances on Terry

Terry (*scared*) Jack! Tall Tom! He's got the Waxifier!
Waxman (*holding the Waxifier up*) I should have done this earlier!

Tall Tom and the others burst in

Tall Tom Terry, we're here.
Waxman (*covering them with the Waxifier*) Don't move, any of you—or I'll waxify you for ever.

They all move towards him

Right! You've asked for it. The boy goes first!

Waxman aims the Waxifier and shoots, but—

Tall Tom It didn't work!
Waxman (*feverishly inspecting the nozzle*) There's something blocking the nozzle—a piece of fluff—there! (*Pulling it free*) It's free! (*The nozzle is pointing towards him*)
Terry (*rushing forward and working the handle*) There!

Waxman Aghhhhhhhhhhhhhhhhhhhhhhhhhhhh! (*He is waxified*)
Floss He's waxified!
Brunhilda (*watching the last jerks*) He's taking a long time to go!

Finally Waxman is still—waxified

Brunhilda It wasn't fluff—it was Floss!
Terry It was fluff—in the Waxifier.
Jack (*to Terry*) Are you all right, Terry?
Tall Tom What?
Brunhilda (*proudly*) Sabotage! Floss bunged up the Waxifier.
Floss (*serenely*) I did it.

> *Brunhilda exits*

Terry Well.
Tall Tom Give me the Waxifier. It must be destroyed.

Terry hands Tall Tom the Waxifier. Tall Tom places it out of the way

Terry Look at the Professor. What a waxwork!
Floss (*sweetly*) Let's melt him down into a long-playing record, and spin him at the wrong speed.
Tall Tom He'd look good in the Waxwork Tent.
Terry He'll be the star attraction.
Jack "The Wickedest Villain of Them All."

The waxwork is wheeled away

Terry Well, we've done. We've found all the eight black pearls and Tall Tom's innocence is proved at last. (*To Jack*) Come on, we'll tell Grandpa! (*He starts to run off*; And then . . .

Jack has not moved

What's the matter, Jack, aren't you coming? (*Carefully*) You don't want to leave the Fair, do you?

There is no reaction from Jack, but Terry understands

Oh, Jack, it's been so exciting. I'll miss you.
Jack Here! (*He pulls the string of black pearls from his pocket with a magical gesture*)
Terry You've threaded the pearls together.

The statue of Lady Melanie is wheeled forward. Terry places them round the neck

It really *is* Lady Melanie's necklace now. How . . .? (*Realizing*) Oh, Jack, of course. You brought Tall Tom to life. I ought to have known—all along. You *are* magic, aren't you?

Grandpa enters

Grandpa Hello, Terry. What have you been up to? Where have you been?

Terry (*running to him*) I've been to the Fair on the Common.

Grandpa (*smiling*) Oh, yes; and I suppose you lay in the grass and dreamed it all.

Terry I didn't!

Grandpa (*seeing the statue*) Good heavens! The Lady Melanie's pearls have been found at last.

Terry And Tall Tom's innocence is proved. I didn't dream it, Grandpa. It really *was* the Adventure of the Age.

The figures of Floss and Tall Tom can be seen near Jack. The Lights begin to fade on the Fairground

(*Waving*) Good-bye, Jack. Good-bye, Floss. Look after him, Tall Tom. Good-bye, Fantastic Fairground.

Mr Barker A Fairground's the world
  For little boys and girls;
  The world is an oyster—
  Search for the pearls.

CURTAIN

FURNITURE AND PROPERTY LIST

NOTE: The following itemizes only such properties as are actually referred to or used in the action. As with the setting, the production can be made as elaborate or as simple as the producer wishes and the facilities permit. Props such as fairground booths, etc. can be either preset and moved into position, or wheeled or carried on and off as required. Props pertaining to a particular character are listed separately under the name concerned.

GENERAL PROPS
Gravestone
Rifle range with rifles, targets and prizes—including 1 purse with a pearl inside
Several small numbered boxes on a stall
Balloons
Hoopla rings
Sweet and Ice-cream stall—including bags of aniseed balls, in one of which is a pearl
Test-Your-Strength machine, with hammer and bell, and pearl concealed on top
Merry-Go-Round
Cut-out to suggest Temple of Mystic East
Waxwork Tent, with odd legs and arms lying about

INDIVIDUAL PROPS

Jack	Rag
	Feather duster
	Oil can
	Torch with colour filter
Waxman	Candy floss
	Large umbrella
	Ice cream
Tall Tom	Pistol
Dr Quack	Bag with bottles of patent medicine
Spivver	"Waxifier" spray (for **Professor Waxman**)
Brunhilda	Large stick of candy floss
Grab Machine	Metal claw hand, levers, sweets and other small objects, among them a pearl
Floss	"Eastern" ring containing pearl
Snakecharmer	Pipe to play
Indian God	Pearl in headdress
Man of Mystery	Crystal ball
Mediaeval Lady	Purse
Elizabethan Lady	Ring

LIGHTING PLOT

NOTE: The following is a simplified plot, confined in the main to cues relevant to the action. Additional effects (e.g. spots to cover the songs) can, of course, be added at the discretion of the producer.

Property fittings required: nil
A bare or open stage

ACT I.

To open: General overall lighting

Cue 1	**Lady Melanie** comes alive *General fade to mere glimmer, with spot on grandpa*	(Page 4)
Cue 2	The **Stranger** exits *Resume overall lighting low key*	(Page 4)
Cue 3	**Jack**: "Keep still, and *watch!*" *Fade up general lighting to full*	(Page 5)
Cue 4	**Dr Quack**: ". . . but never come out." *Fade to shadowy dimness*	(Page 8)
Cue 5	**Jack** and **Terry** rush away *Bring up to general lighting*	(Page 9)
Cue 6	**Terry** and **Jack** exit *Lighting change to emphasise Mystic East Temple*	(Page 19)
Cue 7	**Floss**: "—out of the Snake Pit." *Lighting change to emphasize Snake Pit and Snake*	(Page 19)
Cue 8	**Indian God** enters *Bring up spot on Indian God*	(Page 20)
Cue 9	**Indian God** exits *Revert to full general lighting*	(Page 21)
Cue 10	**Man of Mystery**: ". . . look into my crystal." *Fade to rather sinister, shadowy effect*	(Page 26)
Cue 11	**Man of Mystery** exits *Revert to full general lighting*	(Page 27)

ACT II

To open: General overall lighting

Cue 12	**Jack**: "But the Adventure's not over yet." *Fade to general dimness and deep shadows*	(Page 38)
Cue 13	**Waxman** (*off*): "Search the tent!" *Bring lighting up to about half*	(Page 40)

Cue 14   **Tall Tom:** "Ready, go!"   (Page 42)
            Change to eerie light and use Haunted House special effect

Cue 15   **Terry:** "We found the final clue."   (Page 42)
            Brighten lighting and use zoo special effect

Cue 16   **Waxman:** "I've trapped you in the maze!"   (Page 43)
            Moving light for maze special effect

Cue 17   **Tall Tom** bursts in   (Page 43)
            Cut off whirling lights and bring up general lighting to full

Cue 18   **Terry:** "It really *was* the Adventure of the Age"   (Page 45)
            Slow fade to blackout

MUSICAL NUMBERS

ACT I

1 ROLL UP, ROLL UP (Soloists and Company)
2 ROLL UP, ROLL UP (Mr Barker and Company)
3 WHERE CAN THE NEXT ONE BE? (Jack)
4 THE SWEET-LADY'S SONG (Waxman)
5 WHERE CAN THE NEXT ONE BE? (Jack)
6 WHERE CAN THE NEXT ONE BE? (Jack)
7 WHERE CAN THE NEXT ONE BE (Jack)
8 WHERE CAN THE NEXT ONE BE? (Jack)
9 THE STRONG MAN'S SONG (Waxman)
10 WHERE CAN THE NEXT ONE BE? (Jack)

ACT II

12 ROLL UP, ROLL UP (Mr Barker)
12a ICE-CREAM SONG
13 USHERETTES' DUET (Brunhilda, Floss)
14 HAVE A LITTLE BIT OF HOPE (Mr Barker & Jack)
14a THE ROUNDABOUT SONG (Mr Barker and Waxman)
15 WHERE CAN THE NEXT ONE BE? (Jack)
16 CHASE CHANT

INCIDENTAL MUSIC PLOT

ACT I

Cue 1   **Mr Barker:** "Long before the Fairground ever appeared."   (Page 2)
Comical musical fanfare

Cue 2   **Tall Tom** enters   (Page 4)
Dramatic chords

Cue 3   **Jack:** "Let's start looking, then."   (Page 7)
Fairground music starts up

Cue 4   **Mr Barker:** ". . . silks and satins and *pearls!*"   (Page 18)
Eastern music—fade when girls exit

Cue 5   **Snakecharmer** plays   (Page 20)
Snake pipe music—fade when **Jack** *gets pearl*

Cue 6   **Indian God** enters   (Page 20)
Indian mystery music—fade when **God** *exits*

ACT II

Cue 7   **Floss:** "There's another one to dust."   (Page 33)
Mournful music as **Quack** *is moved off*

Cue 8   **Jack** shines torch on **Tall Tom**   (Page 40)
Strange, tingling music. Continue until **Tall Tom** *speaks*

6/122